In the nig

Story written by Gill Munton
Illustrated by Tim Archbold

Speed Sounds

Consonants   *Ask children to say the sounds.*

f	l	m	n	r	s	v	z	sh	(th)	(ng)
ff	ll	mm	nn	rr	ss	ve	zz			(nk)
	le		kn				s			

b	c	d	g	h	j	p	qu	t	w	x	y	ch
bb	k	dd	gg			(pp)		tt	wh			(tch)
	(ck)											

Each box contains one sound but sometimes more than one grapheme.
*Focus graphemes for this story are **circled**.*

4

Vowels

Ask children to say the sounds in and out of order.

a	e	i	o	u	ay	ee	igh	ow
	ea					y		
at	hen	in	on	up	day	see	high	blow

oo	oo	ar	or	air	ir	ou	oy
zoo	look	car	for	fair	whirl	shout	boy

Story Green Words

Ask children to read the words first in Fred Talk and then say the word.

rats fight grin tight fright wings

bump switch light sight creep

Ask children to say the syllables and then read the whole word.

gob|lin

Ask children to read the root first and then the whole word with the suffix.

witch → witches   tuck → tucked

trick → tricks   flap → flapping

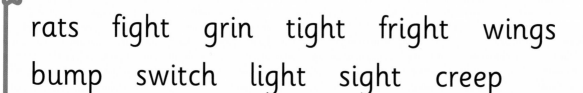

Red Words

Ask children to practise reading the words across the rows, down the columns and in and out of order clearly and quickly.

some	no	all	of
the	your	her	I've
call	me	my	are
we	he	she	want

In the night

Rats creep

in the night

dogs yap

cats fight

witches grin

something's not right!

I am tucked in tight
but I think I just might
get a bit of a fright
in the night.

Goblins play tricks
in the night.
On flapping wings
bats in flight.
Something went bump!
Just switch on the light.

I'm tucked in tight
no goblins in sight
and I feel all right
in the night.

Questions to talk about

Ask children to TTYP for each question using 'Fastest finger' (FF) or 'Have a think' (HaT).

p.8 (FF)   What do rats do in the night?

p.10 (HaT)   How do you think the boy is feeling when he says he might get a bit of a fright in the night?

p.11 (FF)   What do goblins do in the night?

p.11 (FF)   What does he do when something goes bump?

p.12 (HaT)   Why does he feel better by the end of the story?